I Have a Little Dreidel

I Have a Little Dreidel

by Maxie Baum
Illustrated by Julie Paschkis

SCHOLASTIC
New York Toronto London Auckland Sydney
Mexico City New Delhi Hong Kong Buenos Aires

Baum, Maxie.
I have a little dreidel / by Maxie Baum ; illustrated by Julie Paschkis.
p. cm.   "Cartwheel Books."
Summary: An illustrated retelling of the classic Hannukah song, with
directions for playing the dreidel game and a recipe for making latkes.
ISBN 0-545-04587-8
1. Children's songs--Texts. [1. Dreidel (Game)--Songs and music.
2. Hanukkah--Songs and music. 3. Songs.] I. Paschkis, Julie, ill. II. Title.
PZ8.3.B3273Iac 2006   782.42--dc22   2005031318

10 9 8 7 6 5 4 3 2 1   6 7 8 9 10/0

Printed in Singapore 46
First printing, October 2006

For Liz, Melissa, Sheryl, and Grace
— M. B.

For Marcie and her good latkes
— J. P.

I have a little dreidel,
I made it out of clay,
And when it's dry and ready,
Then dreidel I shall play!

Oh, dreidel, dreidel, dreidel,
I made it out of clay;
Oh, dreidel, dreidel, dreidel,
Then dreidel I shall play.

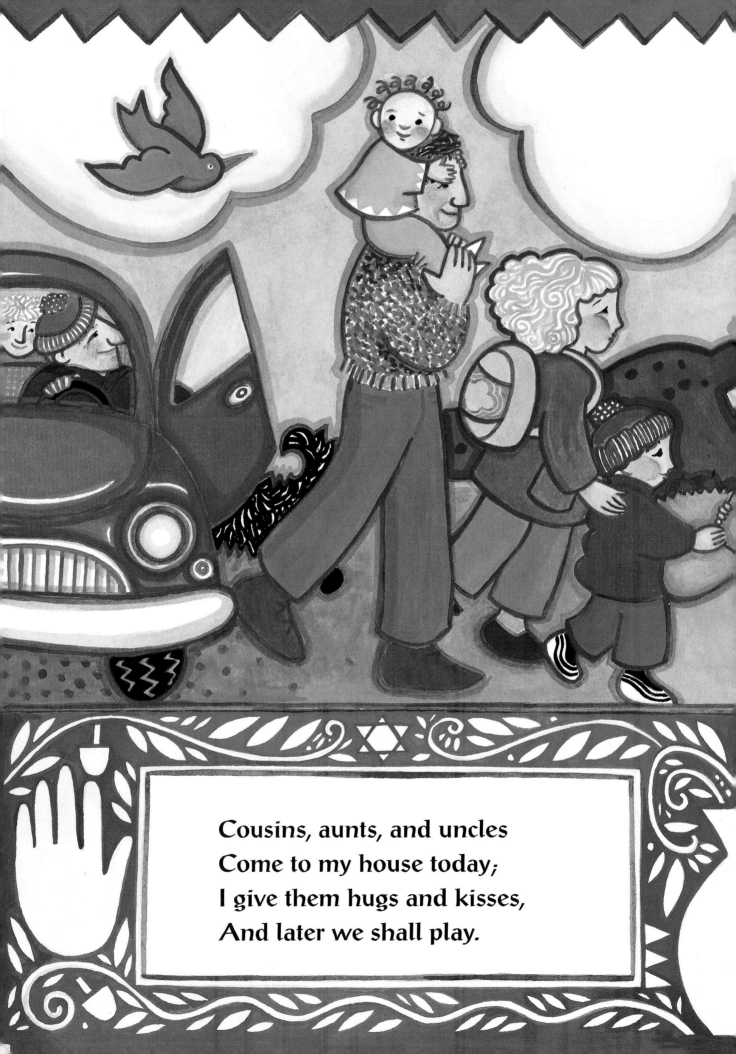

Cousins, aunts, and uncles
Come to my house today;
I give them hugs and kisses,
And later we shall play.

Oh, dreidel, dreidel, dreidel,
I made it out of clay;
Oh, dreidel, dreidel, dreidel,
Then dreidel I shall play.

We gather in the kitchen,
Each and every one;
We're going to make some latkes,
Because it's so much fun.

Oh, dreidel, dreidel, dreidel,
I made it out of clay;
Oh, dreidel, dreidel, dreidel,
Then dreidel I shall play.

The cousins grate potatoes;
That's what we like to do –
We mix matzo and some onions,
Then add an egg or two.

Oh, dreidel, dreidel, dreidel,
I made it out of clay;
Oh, dreidel, dreidel, dreidel,
Then dreidel I shall play.

Mommy fries the latkes
And puts them on a plate;
Supper's almost ready,
And I can hardly wait.

Oh, dreidel, dreidel, dreidel,
I made it out of clay;
Oh, dreidel, dreidel, dreidel,
Then dreidel I shall play.

First we light the candles
Because we celebrate
The victory of the Maccabees—
Tonight we're lighting eight.

Oh, dreidel, dreidel, dreidel,
I made it out of clay;
Oh, dreidel, dreidel, dreidel,
Then dreidel I shall play.

We all go to the table
'Cause now it's time to eat
Our applesauce and latkes;
What a yummy treat!

Oh, dreidel, dreidel, dreidel,
I made it out of clay;
Oh, dreidel, dreidel, dreidel,
Then dreidel I shall play.

Now that supper's over,
we wash and put away;
We gather in the living room—
Now dreidel we shall play.

Oh, dreidel, dreidel, dreidel,
I made it out of clay;
Oh, dreidel, dreidel, dreidel,
Then dreidel I shall play.

The kids sit in a circle—
We all take turns to spin:
Some take some pennies out,
Some put some pennies in.

Oh, dreidel, dreidel, dreidel,
I made it out of clay;
Oh, dreidel, dreidel, dreidel,
Then dreidel I shall play.

It has a lovely body,
With leg so short and thin,
Oh, dreidel, dreidel, dreidel;
It drops and then I win!

Oh, dreidel, dreidel, dreidel,
With leg so short and thin,
Oh, dreidel, dreidel, dreidel;
It drops and then I win!

How to Make

Potato Latkes

You will need a grown-up to help you!

6 medium-sized raw potatoes

1 large raw carrot

1 raw onion

1/4 cup matzo meal

2 raw eggs

vegetable or olive oil

(about 1/4 cup, or as needed)

salt and pepper to taste

Grate the potatoes, carrot, and onion. Mix together in a bowl, then add the matzo meal and eggs. Mix well. Heat the oil. Place large spoonfuls of the mixture into the pan. Cook on both sides until golden brown.

Serve with applesauce.

How to Play

Dreidel

To begin the game, all players get 10–15 objects (nuts, raisins, pennies, etc.). Everyone puts one object in "the pot" (the middle). Each player takes a turn spinning.

Here is what each Hebrew letter on the side of the dreidel stands for:

or **nun** stands for **nisht** or "nothing."
If your dreidel lands on nun, do nothing.

or **gimel** stands for **ganz** or "all."
If your dreidel lands on gimel, take everything in the pot.

or **hay** stands for **halb** or "half."
If you get hay, take half of what's in the pot (plus one, if there's an odd number left).

or **shin** stands for **shtel** or "put in."
If you get shin, put two objects in the pot.

When only one object or none is left in the pot, every player adds one.

When one person has everything, he or she wins!

Dreidel Song